THE
JOY OF MINDFUL
JOURNALING

THE JOY OF MINDFUL JOURNALING

FINDING SERENITY THROUGH CREATIVE EXPRESSION

TARA WARD

ARCTURUS

ARCTURUS

This edition published in 2021 by Arcturus Publishing Limited
26/27 Bickels Yard, 151–153 Bermondsey Street,
London SE1 3HA

Copyright © Arcturus Holdings Limited

ISBN: 978-1-83857-396-6
AD007273US

Printed in China

Contents

AUTHOR'S NOTE

Congratulations for deciding to add more joy into your life! The more difficult your life feels, the more challenges you are facing, the more important it is to find joy. Despite having had a lot of personal loss and sadness over the past ten years, practicing mindfulness has given me joy in a way I wouldn't have believed possible. Often it has come to me at unexpected moments, sometimes in the midst of great sadness. Once you allow yourself to feel joy in a mindful way, it is always available to you, even in the simplest task or experience. And in troubled times, spreading joy is one of the most positive steps we can take.

Find ecstasy in life;
the mere sense of living is joy enough.

Emily Dickinson

Introduction

So welcome to increasing the joy in your life through mindfulness. This is the third mindful journaling book I have written and it differs from *Mindful Journaling* and *Mindfulness Journaling* in that it focusses solely on joy and how to create more of it in your life. Being joyous in a mindful way is different from just feeling happy. When you're being truly mindful all your senses come alive at once and that leads to a deeper experience of joy. The series of exercises laid out over 14 days in this book is designed to let you discover joy on a whole new level, irrespective of your circumstances.

You can know great sadness and still experience joy.

Mindfulness means simply to "be in the moment" and in that process to let go of thoughts/anxieties about the past and future. We can be in the state of mindfulness for a few seconds or stay within it for a longer period; it's up to you. Mindfulness can be beneficial in lots of ways, but in this book we are going to focus on the JOY it can bring you.

Joy can be an underrated word and is often mentioned casually, but to know deep joy is a profound and wonderful experience. I want to help you find such joy through this book.

When you do things
from your soul,
you feel a river moving
in you, a joy.

Rumi

So let's start this introduction with a mini mindfulness moment right now, as you are reading this. Say the word "joy" to yourself, out loud if you can. Repeat it a few times, slowly, and thoughtfully. What does it mean to you?

Jot down below what you experienced when you said the word "joy." Also include any sensations you might have felt in your body and where they were …

a thought and feeling in my mind, something that I know I have experienced before.
Happy memories.
visualising smiling, happy. being min people I love and care for

Well done: a mini mindful moment! You might be surprised by what you felt or thought in an instant. You can return to what you wrote here in future and notice how your attitude may have changed. If you felt very little, please don't worry as we will explore the word "joy" more deeply in exercises to come.

How To Use This Book

The Joy of Mindful Journaling is set out as a 14-day plan for exploring how to create more joy in your life. You don't have to do these exercises on consecutive days; it can be as and when you can find time. To help you further, you'll find both a shorter and longer exercise for each day so it gives you flexibility. You might want to do all the short exercises first—and then return and do the longer ones! Some aspects of a particular exercise might appeal to you more than others. It is totally up to you. Read through the whole of each section once before deciding which exercise you want to try. You will notice that some shorter exercises will lead naturally on to the longer exercise too, if you have time for both.

Since many of the exercises don't take very long, repeat them more than once in the day if you can. Some you could do five or even ten times throughout the day and it would take less than a few minutes.

Some sections include mini exercises at the start. Do them as you go along or return to them later—whatever appeals to you.

Please go through the days in order. The exercises are designed to go deeper as the days progress and to build on the previous day's experience.

Also, please make sure you start with Essential Exercise Day 1: The Breath. It forms the foundation for mindfulness. If you have time to do the Breathing Exercise before each subsequent exercise, this will deepen your mindful experience of joy.

Affirmations

You may have come across Affirmations before. These are short statements, always phrased in a positive form, that you can repeat to yourself at least ten times in one go. You can speak them silently or aloud. You don't need to believe what you say, but your brain will acknowledge them and it can be a powerful method of slowly reprogramming your thoughts into a more helpful and positive space. If you've never tried them before, practice with the Affirmations throughout the book and notice what effect they have on you. Constant repetition is important for success: at least ten repetitions repeated at least ten times per day. Because all Affirmations are short, they are quick and easy to do!

Poetry & Quotes

Let yourself "play" with the poetry and quotes however you wish. Say them aloud or silently—or even sing them! Write them down and have them around you. (You can do this with the Affirmations too.) Share them with others and notice their responses. These are tools to help deepen your experience of mindful joy and it can be fun to see them as a game.

Three Checks

Before you start, here are three important checks:

- Alcohol and mind-altering drugs won't mix well with these exercises

- You will need to be undisturbed for most of these exercises; they only last a short time

- Don't push yourself in any way; it is fine whether you feel a lot or very little. Mindfulness is not a competition!

*To know joy
we need to be in the now
—and to let go of
past and future worries.*

Letting Go

Even though we will be focusing on joy, occasionally emotions/sensations can hit us during mindfulness moments and, if we feel overwhelmed, we may want to wash something away or let it go.

So please try this simple exercise before you move on to Day 1.

LET IT GO EXERCISE

Sit comfortably with both your feet flat on the floor and take a few comfortable breaths. Don't force anything. Notice how your body relaxes a little as you focus on your breathing.

Now ask yourself what "let it go" means to you. What sensation or image comes to you? It could be a washing away, or a flying away, or something shrinking and disappearing. It might be a receding sound or it might be a sensation of release somewhere in your body. It might be a combination of several things.

It doesn't matter what it is because it will be personal to you. Take your time and allow yourself to sink into the sound, sensation, or image.

Say the words silently or out loud to yourself: "Let it go." Repeat them a few times.

Allow whatever you have created to become as strong and vivid as you can. This makes the experience more powerful. Then place yourself into whatever you have created and feel yourself letting go of anything you don't want to hold on to right now. Take your time to experience it fully.

Notice how much lighter and brighter you feel when you have let something go.

When you are ready, slowly open your eyes and make sure your body feels heavy in your seat and your feet are planted firmly on the ground before you get up.

Please return to this exercise whenever you want—at any time of the day. It can become such a helpful tool in letting go of anything that you don't want. In fact, this shedding of unwanted emotions, thoughts, and sensations can be a joyful experience in itself.

Some people find mindfulness exercises very powerful straight away, so it's good to have a technique that gives you some control over whatever you experience.

When you are ready, start with Essential Exercise Day One!

We all live,
but the secret
is to feel alive.

Make a note of your feelings/thoughts about the Letting It Go exercise and also the different ways you choose to release anything you don't want.

DAY ONE
BREATHING

At the forefront of all mindfulness techniques is awareness of breath. It is ironic that something we do without thinking is essential to staying alive! Yet how often do we really stop and focus on our breathing through the day? For many of us, the answer is very rarely, so becoming more aware of your breathing and "becoming friends" with your breath will make all the upcoming mindfulness exercises more enjoyable and easier.

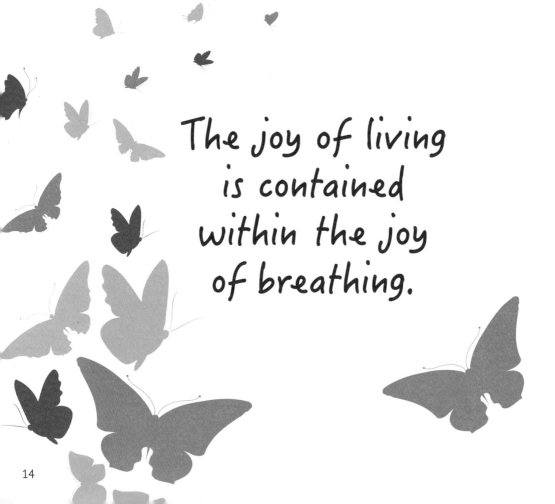

The joy of living is contained within the joy of breathing.

Calling of Breath
by Georgie Ward

A small space within my day
A little time for me
Calmness touched my heart
My breath was calling, calling me

My cosy chair supported me
Amongst filtered shade and sun
This brief time was mine alone
My breath was calling, calling me

My body felt much lighter
Stress flew up and far away
I felt the joy, the peace engulf my soul
and ...
My breath was calling, calling me.

SHORT BREATHING EXERCISE

Sit or stand comfortably with your weight distributed evenly on both feet. If you are sitting, close your eyes if you wish. Take three comfortable, deep breaths. Let your shoulders feel heavy and notice how they don't have to move up and down as you breathe. The breathing action takes place lower down in your ribs as they expand and contract.

Now as you breathe in, say the word "joy" silently to yourself. As you breathe out, repeat the word "joy." Continue this for at least five rounds.

Let your thoughts and feelings come and go as you do this. There is no right or wrong way to respond and you don't have to hold on to anything. Let your reactions ebb and flow with each breath.

Now open your eyes if you've had them closed and make sure that your body feels heavy and grounded. Give your feet a little stamp on the ground; clench and unclench your buttocks a few times.

Make notes opposite about your experience.

What were your initial thoughts and feelings? How did they change after a few breaths? Note down any images, sensations, sounds, smells, or tastes.

Before we get into the Longer Breathing Exercise, I'd like to tell you something about our breathing equipment! You probably know already that when we breathe in through our nose or mouth, the air travels down into our two lungs, located behind our ribcage. Our lungs are surprisingly large and inside them are little "branches" (bronchioles) at the end of which are tiny air sacs (alveoli). There are up to 480 million minuscule alveoli in our lungs! Look at the diagram below. Even when exercising intensely, humans tend to use only up to 70 percent of their lung capacity, so when we breathe in we tend not to inflate all of our mini sacs. Becoming more mindful of your breathing on a daily basis gives you the chance to breathe more deeply.

Really study the diagram below and take a moment to appreciate the beauty and complexity of our breathing system. Then consider the quote opposite and try the Affirmation (repeating it ten times silently or aloud) before you continue with the Deeper Breathing Exercise.

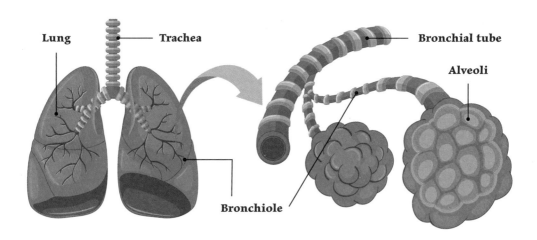

Lung — Trachea — Bronchial tube

Alveoli

Bronchiole

If you
half breathe,
you only
half live.

AFFIRMATION:

Every breath I take
is joyful.

LONGER BREATHING EXERCISE

Sit or lie down. If sitting, have an upright position, with your arms resting comfortably and both feet flat on the floor. If lying, lie flat on your back if possible, with pillows under your head and/or knees—whatever is most comfortable for you. Let your arms rest comfortably by your side and have your legs slightly apart, feet facing outward. Close your eyes.

Firstly, let yourself settle. Wriggle a bit if you need to. Gently stretch your muscles. Release tension by sighing or yawning. When you're ready, start to focus on the breath going in and out of your body. Don't try to breathe more deeply or tell yourself to relax. Just let yourself be and focus solely on your breath.

Feel the air coming in through your nose or mouth and imagine it going down into your lungs. Visualize it traveling through all the bronchioles and then into the minuscule alveoli "sacs." Picture them inflating as you breathe in and then deflating as you breathe out. Stay like this for as long as you like.

Then say the word "joy" to yourself silently. Welcome whatever images or sensations come; let them flow. As you breathe in, imagine joy coming into you on your breath, going into your lungs, and the word filling all your alveoli. As you breathe out, imagine the word "joy" seeping through all of your body. Notice how it makes you feel. Enjoy the experience.

When you are ready, slowly return your attention to your physical body and notice how heavy it feels, especially where it makes contact with a surface. Open your eyes, stretch, and take your time before making notes opposite.

What were your early feelings and thoughts? How did they change as you progressed through the exercise? What was your first reaction to the word "joy" and how did it shift as you continued? Apart from writing down what you felt during the exercise, also make a note about how you were left feeling and thinking at the end of it.

Well done on your Day 1 Breathing exercise—whether you chose the shorter or longer version! If you can do this several times during the day, that will help you on your mindfulness journey into joy.

In fact, I'm going to suggest you return to this whenever you can—even as you enjoy other exercises along the way. Or if you have the time and would like to, repeat Exercise 1 for a few days before going on to Exercise 2.

Awareness of breath is the foundation of mindfulness and the more you become friends with your breathing and find joy in simple awareness of breath, the more profound you will find all the other exercises.

Remember that the journey itself is a joy—with mindfulness we are never trying to get anywhere, simply to focus on exactly where we are in the here and now. That in itself is joyful with no pressure or expectations attached.

Let us leave this Breathing section for now with the uplifting and practical thought below ...

Awareness
of breath is
the cheapest way
to find
inner peace.

DAY TWO
TOUCH

A part of our body is touching something every second of every day, yet how often do we stop to really notice what all these different surfaces feel like? Just think, from the moment we are conceived, we are always touching something. It is actually impossible for us not to be touching something at all times. It's a fascinating thought that if we stop to add up how many surfaces any part of our body touches from the moment we wake until the moment we fall asleep, it would be hundreds, if not thousands. Yet many, perhaps most, of those sensations we tend to brush over and not really notice or fully experience.

Humans have two touch systems. One gives us facts such as location and movement and that is called discriminative touch. The second is the emotional touch system and that affects a different part of our brain that is related to bonding socially. This emotional touch is less cognitive of where the touch is happening; it is more about how it feels.

Now reread the two paragraphs opposite and then write below what thoughts and feelings you are having about the sense of touch. What does it make you want to touch?

AFFIRMATION:

All I touch brings me joy.

SHORT TOUCH EXERCISE

Sit comfortably and close your eyes. First, let the fingertips of one hand touch the other hand and gently brush/rub those fingertips against each other. What does that feel like? It might surprise you how sensitive they are and how much you feel suddenly.

Close your eyes and focus on the sensations. Make the touch even finer and more delicate. How does that increase sensation?

Now place one hand gently over your arm and say silently to yourself "love and joy." Place your other hand on your other arm and repeat the words. How does that make you feel?

Breathe in the word "joy" as you did in Exercise 1 and as you breathe out imagine the word being released through your fingertips and into your arm.

When you're ready, open your eyes and gently rub your arms and hands.

Be honest as you write down your thoughts and feelings. Sometimes it is hard to find the right words to express emotion. You can also draw if images feel more appropriate than words. And remember, if you felt very little that is fine. There is no contest in mindfulness. Would you say your mindful touch experience was a discriminative or emotional touch? Why?

LONGER TOUCH EXERCISE

Choose an item that you would like to practice touching in a mindful manner. Choose something to which you are drawn. It might be because someone special gave it to you or that you love the look or shape of it. Place it in front of you.

Start by closing your eyes and focusing on your breathing. As you relax, breathe in the word "joy" and breathe it out.

Then bring the fingertips of one hand to meet the fingertips of your other hand. Very, very gently brush the fingertips together. Feel the wonder of those fingertips and how many objects they touch each day and what they do for you. Feel gratitude for them. Breathe the word "joy" into them. Thank them. You may find yourself smiling. Hold your hands together and give them a gentle squeeze.

Now slowly wrap your arms around yourself and give yourself a soft hug, repeating the word "joy" as you do so. Really notice what you feel like. What parts of your body are touching each other now? What sensations and thoughts are you having?

Then, when you are ready, unwrap your arms and pick up your item. Gently hold it in your hands in whatever way feels comfortable. Stroke it gently with your thumb, then with each other finger individually. What fingers are most sensitive?

As you hold the item, give yourself permission to feel joy for whatever this object means to you. Love and joy are inextricably mingled. Let yourself feel whatever you would like to feel. Let whatever thoughts you have come and go and flow through you.

Really notice the texture of the object and how it feels against your fingertips/hands. When you are ready, place it back down again, gently clasp your hands together, and then release them. Make notes opposite when you are ready.

This can be a powerful exercise. Write below what you experienced, especially noticing which fingers and parts of your hand were particularly sensitive. What did joy mean to you in connection with this object? How did touching the object that mindfully differ from just touching it casually? Remember you can use your Let It Go exercise in the Introduction if anything feels too much.

Once you start to awaken your sense of touch in a mindful way, it is a wonderful, joyous experience. Suddenly everything becomes so much more interesting. I remember being fascinated by how soft my inner wrist felt and wondering how I could never have noticed it before. (Touch yours delicately and you'll see what I mean!)

This mindful exploration of touch can become a lifetime joy and doesn't need to be restricted to an exercise you do sometimes. Pause at any moment during any day and enjoy the different sensations of touch. What can you discover? Notice if touching certain things gives you particular joy and try to have those things around you more frequently. And notice how touching people you love is more joyful when you do so mindfully.

To know joy,
receive
a loving touch.

DAY THREE
SMELL

As one of our five senses, smell may be something we don't think about much, unless the odor is particularly appealing or disgusting! So how does smell work? Humans have about 450 different types of olfactory receptors that work out different scents and we can distinguish approximately 10,000 separate odors (some scientists say this number is even greater). No two humans experience smell in the same way; we are all individual.

What I find powerful about smell is how it can transport me instantly back to a memory I thought I had forgotten. It will happen unexpectedly and often make me feel very emotional. Yet I hadn't thought about that incident for many years. Smell seems to do that more often to me than my other senses and I have friends and family who say the same thing. This may be because our olfactory senses are right in the middle of our brain, so we have strong neural connections with scents.

We can smell because we have receptors high up in our nose that odor molecules cling to and those receptors then send messages to our brain. Most scents have a complex collection of odor molecules: Chocolate, for instance, has hundreds of different ones!

AFFIRMATION:

I breathe in the
scent of joy.

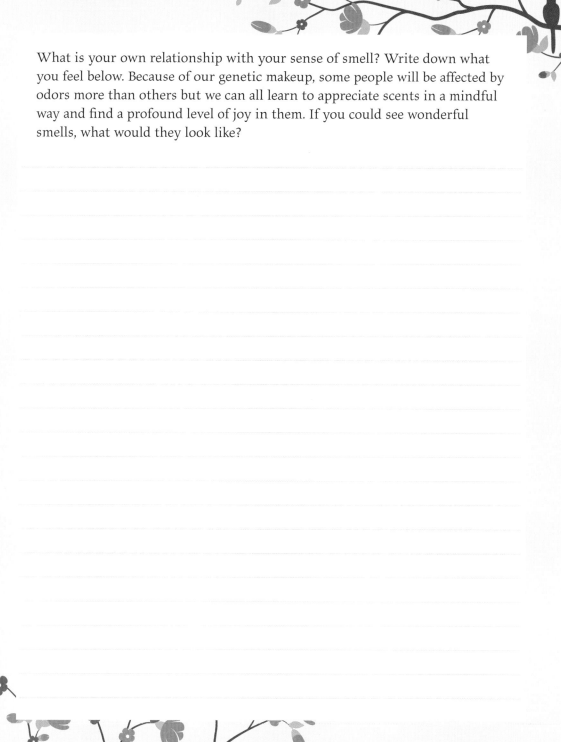

What is your own relationship with your sense of smell? Write down what you feel below. Because of our genetic makeup, some people will be affected by odors more than others but we can all learn to appreciate scents in a mindful way and find a profound level of joy in them. If you could see wonderful smells, what would they look like?

SHORT SMELL EXERCISE

Choose something which has a smell that you like. It could be a plant or perfume or something edible. It doesn't matter. Hold it in your hands.

Sit or stand comfortably and take a moment to focus on your breathing. You can close your eyes if you are sitting. Breathe in the word "joy" and breathe it out.

First, touch the object gently and stroke it, letting your sense of touch be a joy in itself. Now lift the object close to your nose and breathe in deeply. Let the smell fill your lungs. What is the first scent you get; how would you describe it? Release that breath and then take another, a little more deeply this time. Notice how it differs. Where in your body do you feel the pleasure of this scent?

Repeat this one more time and then, as you breathe out, take the object away from your nose. Open your eyes and reorient yourself in the room before you make some notes.

Take your time as you describe the smells: the first, second, and third. How did they differ? What did you feel/think about the object when you had finished? Also notice how you felt/thought when stroking the object. Did you do that mindfully as well?

LONGER SMELL EXERCISE

Sit comfortably in an upright chair with both feet flat on the ground. Close your eyes and focus on your breathing as you let your body settle and relax. When you are ready, bring the word "joy" into you as you breathe in and carry it down into your lungs. Breathe the word out.

After a few deep, easy breaths, cup your hands and place them both over your nose. Slowly breathe in and out. Notice what you smell first. How would you describe it?

Now think about what your hands do every day: the endless tasks they have to perform and how well they do them. What have your hands done already today? Realize how grateful you are for their helpful dexterity. Thank your hands. Be full of appreciation for them.

Breathe into your palms more deeply. What are you smelling now? After a few more slow breaths, kiss your hands very gently. Kiss different parts of them, gently and carefully, thanking them as you do so. Notice how your sense of touch is heightened as you first breathe in their scent and then kiss them. Two senses together.

When you are ready, place your hands back down in your lap and open your eyes. Take a moment to reorient yourself, making sure your feet and buttocks all feel heavy against the surfaces they are resting upon.

This can be an unexpectedly emotional exercise. If it made you feel uncomfortable too, that's fine. Take your time as you try to describe your experience. It can be hard to define scents sometimes. How did your hands feel being kissed? What gave you the most joy? Draw images instead of writing words if this helps you to express yourself better.

You may notice how your joy of touch and smell overlapped during these exercises, until you weren't sure which sense was most powerful. That is normal. As you go through the days, you will see how the senses can all work together and make your mindful experiences profoundly joyful. We are only beginning the journey!

There are some suggestions to enhance your olfactory joy:

- visit a spice store
- walk through a rose garden
- experiment with essential oils
- go into a bakery
- walk where grass has just been cut

Start to notice scents around you more mindfully. Smell things you wouldn't normally. What does your pen smell like? Your phone? Then try to spend time with scents you love. What are your favourite floral scents? What perfumes or essential oils? Fruits and vegetables have amazing smells. What do you like most?

DAY FOUR
TASTE

It seems logical to move forward on to taste now, as smell and taste are closely linked. This is because they both use the same type of receptors in our body. You can smell a food being prepared that you love and immediately want to taste it. Conversely, you might notice that if you have a heavy cold you can't taste food very much; people with no sense of smell can't taste fully.

It is generally accepted we have four taste distinctions: sweet, sour, bitter, and salty. Below is a diagram that shows where on the tongue we most experience these flavors. Yet it is more complicated than that as we can also distinguish between cool and hot—spicy, not temperature—because we know the difference between a cool sprig of mint and a hot chilli pepper, for example. Molecular biologists also discovered recently that we have a "savory" taste ability too (called *umami*), for foods such as soya, cheese, and meat.

So given how our ability to taste is so clever, what would you like to taste mindfully and joyfully?

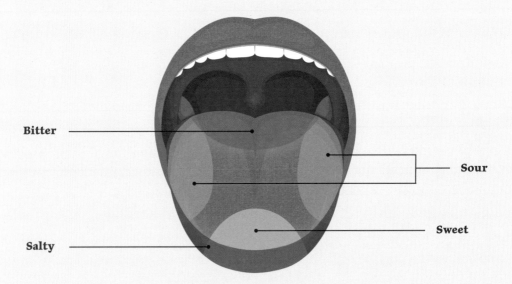

Bitter

Sour

Sweet

Salty

AFFIRMATION:

I taste my food
with joy.

There is no love sincerer
than the love of food.

G.B. Shaw, Man and Superman

SHORT TASTE EXERCISE

Choose a food you love eating—preferably uncooked—that you can also touch with your hands and place a small quantity of it in front of you. Now sit comfortably and take a moment to breathe and relax. Remember the word "joy" as you breathe in; release it on the out breath.

Now pick up your chosen food item and hold it. Gently stroke it. What are you experiencing? Now smell it; notice how that makes you react. Then place it in your mouth and hold it there. Close your eyes if you wish. What are you tasting, if anything? Slowly move it to different parts of your tongue. What happens? Are you still smelling it?

Lastly, bite or suck the food gently and slowly. When is the flavor fully released? How does that moment of finally enjoying the taste make you feel? Where are you feeling this? Where are you tasting it on your tongue? Try to keep it in your mouth for as long as possible before you finally swallow. What does swallowing it feel like?

Notice if the taste lingers afterward or dissipates quickly.

How much more flavor did you experience from eating the food slowly? (Sometimes people find it frustrating because they're used to eating quickly. If that happened to you, it's fine. Just make a note of it.) If you could work out where you felt the taste on your tongue, check back on the tongue diagram and see if that was accurate for you. Ask yourself what level of joy you reached in eating this way. How could you enhance it further?

LONGER TASTE EXERCISE

Choose a very small quantity of a food you love that you can also hold. For example, if it is a strawberry, cut it in half. If it is a carrot, take a small sliver. Then wash your hands.

Sit upright on a chair with the food beside you. Have both your feet flat on the ground. Close your eyes. Settle yourself and breathe deeply.

Now with the little finger of one hand gently, very gently, open your mouth and touch the tip of your tongue. Run your finger delicately along the outside edge of both sides. What does it feel like? Let your finger explore underneath the tongue. How does it differ to the touch? Check out if parts of the tongue feel different from others.

As you explore, consider how your tongue and mouth are miracle feats of engineering that, among other tasks, make food a delight and allow you to enjoy a vital element in survival: eating. How often do you feel gratitude for this part of your body? Give thanks now.

When you are ready, open your eyes, pick up your chosen food, and hold it gently. Stroke it. Really notice what it feels like. Think about where it was grown/created. Close your eyes again and smell it. Think about the journey it has been on to find its way to you. Thank those responsible for making it happen; feel joy for the wonder of nature that has been part of the process of creating it.

Now put the food in your mouth and just hold it there, savoring the texture. Roll it on to different parts of your tongue and see what that is like. What is the sensation? What parts of your tongue are most responsive?

Notice the explosion of tastes as you finally bite into it, chew or suck slowly, and then as you swallow finally, really feel the food disappearing down your throat. Give thanks again for the process involved in creating the food and to your body for making it so enjoyable to eat. See if the taste lingers after you have swallowed.

Try to remember all your sensations as you make notes. Take your time. What was it like to touch your mouth and tongue so carefully? Where on your tongue did you experience the most flavor? Look back at the mouth diagram and see if it relates. What part of the exercise was the most profound for you? What gave you the most joy? Why? Did the food taste as you expected it to when you ate it so slowly? What else would you like to eat mindfully now?

The Joy of Taste
by Georgie Ward

In the cosy cafe
A comfy chair to relax
The colorful tray placed in front
Crispy vegetables, cheese, and nuts
Wholesome bread lightly buttered
Mini desserts of many flavors
Chocolate, caramel, strawberry
Meringue, lemon, cinnamon, and apple
Gratitude spreads
throughout my body
Taste buds tingle
Lips are moist
The joy of taste consumes me
before I even take a bite.

The experience of really tasting food properly can be so joyous, and the more we continue to do it, the more joy it gives us. The act of appreciating our food sources, eating more slowly and chewing more, is also better for our digestion and can add to our general relaxation.

List your favorite foods below and the circumstances in which you most enjoy eating them. Write down your experience with any new foods you try too.

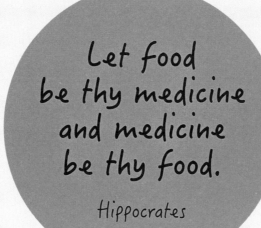

Let food
be thy medicine
and medicine
be thy food.

Hippocrates

The gentle art of gastronomy
is a friendly one.
It hurdles the language barrier,
makes friends among civilised people
and warms the heart.

Samuel Chamberlain

DAY FIVE
SIGHT

Who, on seeing a blind person, has not been grateful for their sight? And then, a little while later, totally forgotten their gratitude and taken it for granted again?

When we are mindful with our sight and choose to see things in a profound way, it helps us to stay longer in a place of gratitude and also to experience a wondrous kind of joy that often we don't allow ourselves.

What are the sights you most enjoy that give you joy? Make a list of them below. Take your time and try to include as many as you can.

My Joyous Sights

Everything has beauty, but not everyone sees it.

Confucius

Excellent. Hopefully you have created a good list. Perhaps you didn't find it that difficult. How lovely you have all those sights that give you joy already. You are well on your way to mindful joy with sight.

Now you have thought of what you enjoy seeing, we are going to explore sight in a different way. We are going to find joy in seeing things in a way we haven't properly "seen" before.

AFFIRMATION:

Seeing is joy.

SHORT SIGHT EXERCISE

Sit or stand comfortably. You could also lie down for this if you want. Focus on your breath for a few moments, concentrating on the word "joy."

When you are ready, transfer your sight and attention to the inner crook of your arm. As you look at it, touch it gently and then sniff it. If you feel like it, you could even lick it. When you have noticed your reactions to this, let your other senses recede and simply study the crook of your arm.

Really study it. How would you describe the texture of your skin? How many different textures are there? Now think about the colors. If you had to paint a picture of this part of you, what colors would you be using?

What does this part of the arm do for you on a daily basis? Feel appreciation for its abilities. What is going on under the skin? What tissues, muscles, and bones are under there? How complex is this small part of our body? How miraculous is its makeup?

Give thanks for your amazing arm.

When you're ready make some notes.

What surprised you most about what you saw? It might be the colors and textures. Or perhaps thinking about the anatomical beauty of your arm affected you. What aspect of this gave you the most joy? If you felt a little strange, giving thanks for a part of your body you hadn't thought much about before, that is fine too.

LONGER SIGHT EXERCISE

Choose something small from nature to study. It could be a blade of grass or a leaf, a small stone or stick, or a petal from a flower—anything you would like to "see" fully.

Sit upright with your feet flat on the floor. Settle, close your eyes, and focus on your breathing. Take the word "joy" in with your breath and allow yourself a little smile. Sit in comfort for a while and relax.

When you're ready, open your eyes and look at your chosen piece of nature. Engage your other senses in a mindful way too: Touch it gently, sniff it, even lick it if you want. Notice the effect that has on you.

Now look at it as if you don't know what it is and you have never seen it before. How would you describe its colors, shape, and textures?

After a little while, close your eyes briefly and try to remember what your object looks like in your mind's eye. Then open your eyes again and study it once more. What did you miss? What renewed joy are you seeing now? Repeat this, closing and opening your eyes again, and discover something else. What do you like most about your object?

As you keep appreciating this piece of nature's gift with your eyes, ask yourself what you know about where it has come from. What form did it take when it first began to exist? How old might it be? What did it need to survive? How might it have been tended by others and how did it end up with you now? Allow yourself a sense of wonder as you think about its life journey. What will happen to it after you finish looking at it? How does its journey continue?

How can you relate your own life's journey to this piece of nature? How are you miraculous and special just like your object? Give thanks for your object but also give thanks for your own journey in life.

Finish by soaking in everything you can about your object with your eyes. When you're ready, put it down and make some observations.

You may be taken aback by just how much you have seen and understood—
or you might not have seen much differently. If it's the latter, you can try
the exercise again with a different object. Then take your time and try to
encapsulate all your thoughts below and overleaf. Describe your object as
thoroughly as you can. When you have finished, put the object back in your
eyeline and look at it again. What more do you see now?

The ability to truly "see" and to become full of wonder and joy is something you can cultivate. Go back to the list you made at the beginning of this section and ask yourself how many of those choices you have actually "seen" in the same way you saw your arm or nature object. What would you most like to see more deeply? Practice it when you can.

You can repeat the shorter exercise with other parts of your body too.

If you want to do something truly joyous with someone you love and trust, sit down opposite each other and look into each other's eyes for at least one full minute. Look at them as though you are seeing them for the first time. It can be a very emotional—and wonderful—experience.

The real voyage of discovery consists,
not in seeking new landscapes,
but in having new eyes.

Marcel Proust

Vision is the art of
seeing things invisible.

Jonathan Swift

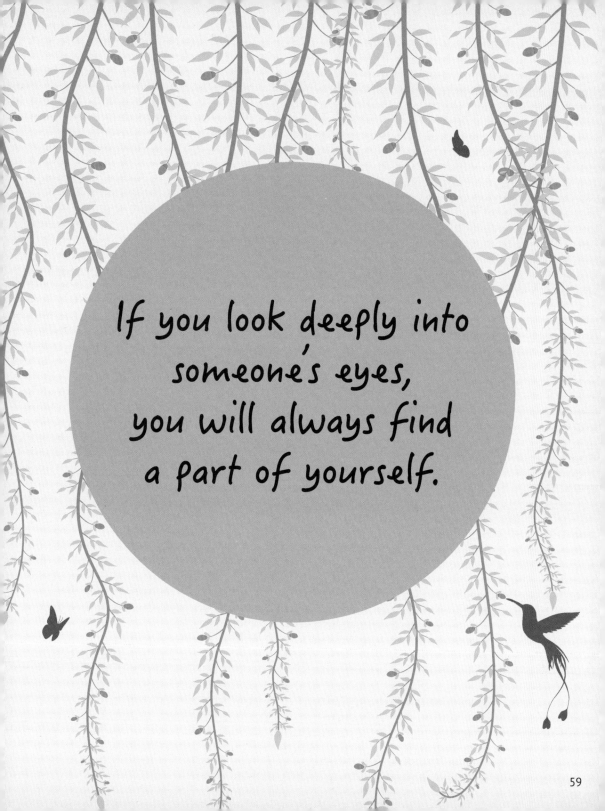

If you look deeply into
someone's eyes,
you will always find
a part of yourself.

DAY SIX
HEARING

Many might say the worst sense you could lose would be your sight, but a wise friend of mine once said "hearing" and when I asked why, they said without sound you can end up so disconnected from everyone else and that never to hear music or nature again would break their spirit. It really made me reconsider how important our sense of hearing is to our daily wellbeing.

The joy of a loved one's voice or our favorite song—how wonderful are they to hear? Yet again, this is a sense we can easily take for granted.

As I write this, I can hear birds singing outside my window. I paused just now to close my eyes and hear them: The richness and variety of sounds are beautiful. They fill my heart with joy. Even though I know how important moments like this are, I still have to remind myself to have them.

Some people are very sensitive to sounds and have naturally acute hearing. Others have a lot of noise around them and don't really hear it. Some crave silence; others want music or sounds around them most of the time. What is your preference? Music is very important to some. Did you know when you listen to music, your heartbeat can sync to its rhythm?

Listen to hear, not to speak.
Therein lies joy.

There's music in the sighing of a reed;
There's music in the gushing of a rill;
There's music in all things, if men had ears:
Their earth is but an echo of the spheres.

Lord Byron

AFFIRMATION:

I stop to listen
and I hear joy.

SHORT HEARING EXERCISE

Try to find a quiet place without the fear of interruption. Choose a piece of music or a sound you enjoy listening to and have it beside you, ready to play. Sit and relax, focusing on your breathing for a moment. Let a wave of the word "joy" wash over and through you as you breathe in the word.

Now turn on the music/sounds and close your eyes. Continue to breathe deeply. Imagine the sound waves coming into your ears as you breathe in. How do your ears feel as they absorb the sounds? Where do those sounds go in your body? What are the sensations? How do they make you feel? It is fine if you find yourself smiling and/or swaying to the sounds.

As you enjoy what you are hearing, try to shut off to any other noise around you and focus purely on your chosen sound. To help you, try to work out how many different pitches or tones you are actually hearing. Is the volume constant or does it vary? Realize that you have a complex and wonderful hearing system that can distinguish between those sounds.

How many different sounds do you have to listen to all the time and how hard does your body work to understand them all, so that your brain and body can navigate you safely through each day? It only gets to shut off when we sleep. How amazing is that thought?

Focus back on your sounds now, with renewed appreciation for how you are able to listen. Finish off by giving thanks for your hearing system and perhaps also thanking the creator of the sounds you were listening to.

What did you notice most about this exercise? What gave you the greatest joy? How did thinking about your own hearing system and what it has to do all the time make you feel? What surprised you? You might have found it hard to focus or to hear the different nuances; that is fine. If you discovered the piece you chose didn't make you feel as you were expecting, make notes below of what other pieces you would like to listen to mindfully.

Before we move on to the longer breathing exercise, let's take a quick look at how our hearing system works. It's a surprisingly complex system. Study the diagram below.

You will see there are several specific stages sound takes once it enters our ears, before our brain processes it and lets us know what it is. And all that happens in less than a second. Isn't that amazing? Think about how much we listen to every day, whether we want to or not, and how hard these parts of our body have to work, all day, every day. When we sleep, our ears are still taking in the sounds because they can never shut off, but at least our brain doesn't process the sounds because it is resting.

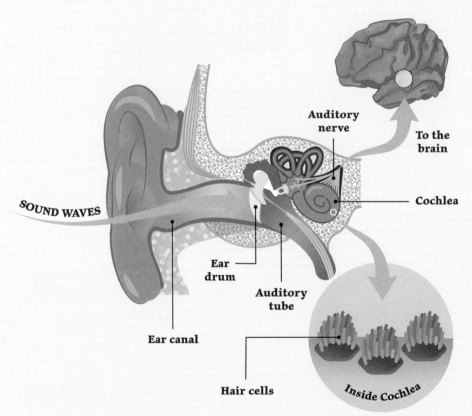

When you have absorbed the ear diagram and understood how you hear
sound, try the longer hearing exercise on the next page.

LONGER HEARING EXERCISE

Try to find a quiet environment without a lot of noise. Sit or lie comfortably. Close your eyes and tune in to your breathing. Once you feel yourself settle and relax, then let the word "joy" come into you as you breathe in. Feel it filling and uplifting you.

Now tune in to the sounds around you right now. There might be a lot or it could be relatively quiet. There will always be something you can hear if you listen intently enough: a distant plane, train or car, the faint hum of electricity, voices, a dog barking, birds tweeting, wind in the trees. There are many other sounds out there too. What can you hear? Take your time and try to distinguish between them all. Notice if some sounds are more pleasing to you.

Once you have heard everything you can, focus closely on the route those sounds are taking. Think about the journey: in through both ears, through the ear canal to your eardrum. Your eardrum vibrates with each sound and sends it to those three tiny bones in your middle ear. These bones amplify the vibrations and pass them on to your inner ear. Your inner ear has tiny hair cells that release neurochemical messages and your auditory nerve carries these to your brain to translate. What can you sense in your ears now you know all this is happening?

Let yourself feel the wonder and joy of this complex process that your body does all the time for you. Enjoy every sound you can hear now and appreciate how you can hear it. Realize how grateful you are for your hearing, whatever the sounds are around you.

When you are ready, open your eyes again, focus on an object in the room, and make sure you are grounded before you get up.

What was the most powerful aspect of that experience? Note down what you could sense in your body of the journey your hearing takes. List everything you could hear. What else might you have heard if you had focused even more? What gave you the greatest pleasure? How could you have more of that in your life? What else would you like to listen to mindfully?

Discovering what your hearing can actually do and how you may not have appreciated it fully before, makes hearing mindfully such a joy. It is fascinating how the most mundane sounds become rather beautiful when you realize the journey they take inside you.

And it means the sounds you love already become even more precious. You might like to finish off this section by making a list below of the sounds you love and committing to having them around you more often.

Sounds That Give Me Joy:

There is no such thing as silence
because we can always
hear our own heartbeat.

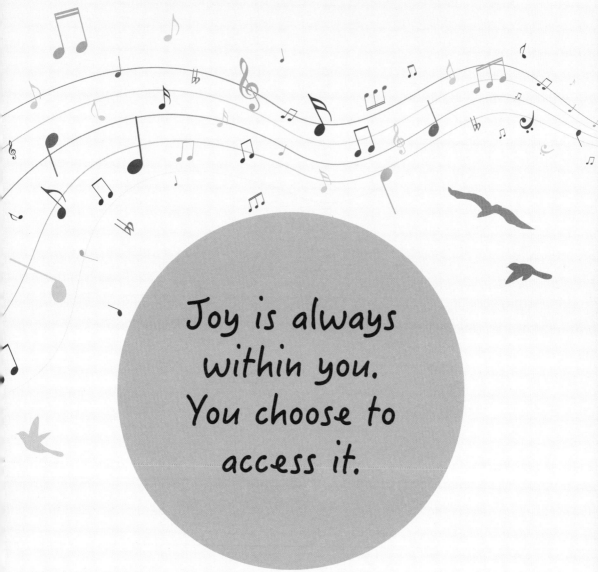

Joy is always
within you.
You choose to
access it.

DAY SEVEN
FEELING

You may think you have done a lot of feeling already through activating your senses during these last six days! And you probably have. In this section you are going to consciously focus on your actual feeling of joy and what it means to you, because everyone experiences joy in their own, unique way.

You may have noticed already that when you've had moments of joy during the exercises, it has been hard to describe them. Joy is such a simple three-letter word and yet the emotions of it can seem impossible to explain. In order to make joy seem more tangible, we are going to explore the feeling associated with it.

Earlier in my Author's Note, I mentioned that having a really difficult time needn't exclude you from having moments of joy. Here is a personal example:

It was nearing the end of my husband's life after a long illness and we had been having hot, dry weather for what seemed like weeks. Suddenly it rained and I opened the windows to let in air. I breathed in deeply. The smell of wet earth and leaves hit me and I felt a totally unexpected rush of pure joy and pleasure at its scent. It felt uplifting and cleansing. I paused to breathe it in and out several times and then returned to reality with a lighter heart and a smile on my face. It was such a welcome respite and by allowing myself that moment to feel something fully, I felt healed in some way.

So joy is not something to be experienced only when we are cheerful and life is good. It is much more profound.

The power of joy helps to dissolve pain.

We have to be mindful, i.e. we have to be present in that moment, to allow ourselves the opportunity to feel that joy. Using the example opposite, if I had thrown open the window and then rushed straight to another task, I would have missed that moment of joy. Notice also how breathing mindfully was a big factor in my experience too.

And please know it isn't about being slow and taking ages to do everything because that would be difficult when most of us have such busy lives. It is purely about committing to the moment we are in, pausing to take a deep breath, and letting all our senses fully enjoy that moment. It is quite simple, isn't it?

The more we rush everywhere, the more we stop ourselves from feeling. Some therapists say the reason we rush around so much is because we are trying to avoid certain feelings. If we keep really busy, we can't think too much. I suspect there is some truth in that.

In this section, you are going to pause to feel something that gives you joy, so the experience will be a pleasant one.

When minds and hearts are open joy comes flowing in.

To explore the feeling of joy more easily, you are going to revisit a happy moment and experience it again. Recalling a joyful instance is sometimes an easier way to connect fully with your feelings.

So close your eyes and ask yourself what moments have given you great joy so far in your life. You don't need to focus on them in depth, just acknowledge them as a moment of joy and continue thinking. When you're ready, write down as many as you can think of below.

My Joyful Moments

AFFIRMATION:

I feel joy
every day.

Open yourself
to the joy of now.

SHORT FEELING EXERCISE

Choose a joyful moment from the list you made on page 72. Sit or lie comfortably, close your eyes, and focus on your breathing for several breaths.

When you feel relaxed, let your chosen joyful memory replay itself for you. Take your time. Remember to let all your senses take part: What does it feel, smell, taste, sound, look like?

As the memory builds and the sensations increase, let yourself be fully immersed in it. Notice if one sense feels more powerful than another.

Ask yourself what you are actually feeling. Where in your body are you feeling it? Try to clarify the sensations: Are they flowing or still? Bright or muted? Sharp or soft? Noisy or quiet?

Stay with your feeling of joy for as long as you wish and then when you are ready, slowly withdraw yourself from the memory. Open your eyes and make sure you are fully "back in the room" after your trip down memory lane.

Depending on the memory you chose, you might be feeling emotional still. Describe your feelings using all of your senses. What senses seem stronger than others? Try to use adjectives as much as possible to clarify what the feeling of joy actually means to you. It is different for everyone, so make yours as personal and specific as you can. As you write, you may find the moment of joy washing over you again. That is lovely. Enjoy it!

LONGER FEELING EXERCISE

Choose one of your joyful memories from your list to focus upon. Then sit or lie comfortably and close your eyes. Spend a minute or two focusing on your breathing first. Let your breath deepen naturally and enjoy the feeling of relaxation spread through you. When your body feels pleasantly heavy and comfortable, turn your thoughts to your joyful memory.

Go through all your senses as you recall it. What does it look like? What can you touch within this memory? What scents are you aware of? What taste is part of this moment? What can you hear?

As all your senses intensify, let your feeling of joy expand and grow. Where is it growing? How is it part of you? Is it inside or outside your body?

Now let yourself step into the memory itself. So rather than seeing it in your mind's eye, enter into the moment and feel yourself completely in it again. How does that make you feel? What thoughts are you having?

Let yourself completely relive this moment of joy all over again. Relish it. Let it wash over and through you. Smile or laugh or do whatever is natural for you.

Keep all your senses alive and simply notice if some are stronger than others. Now you are part of the memory again, more feelings and sensations may come flooding through. Enjoy them.

After a while, try to focus in on how you are really feeling and where you feel it in your body. What does joy feel like for you? Is the energy soft or sharp? Pulsing or still? Does it feel strong or subtle? Is it like a flutter or more of a beat?

Spend as much time as you can immersed in the feeling of joy and then, when you feel ready, slowly withdraw yourself from the joyful memory. See yourself stepping out of it and see it recede into the distance. Watch it disappear. Take a few slow breaths, and then slowly open your eyes. Take some time to reorient yourself before you start writing.

As you make notes, be as specific as you can about where in your body you felt your joy and exactly how it felt. Use as many appropriate adjectives as you can. Try to write slowly and thoughtfully and don't rush. If you feel a little overwhelmed by the exercise, focus on your breathing for a few minutes to ground and balance yourself again. Remember you can draw images if the appropriate words are hard to find.

This section can be particularly sensitive and private so it is fine if you take a while to work out what is happening for you. You may want to stay in this section for more than a day and think about it for a while. There is no rush to complete this book, so feel free to linger here.

Our emotions are delicate and feelings of joy can be very emotional. Once we give ourselves permission to express our feelings fully through all our senses, it can be a very powerful experience. It might also show us that we don't express ourselves fully as often as we might and that the power of mindfulness can help us to do so more often.

Please be gentle with yourself and remember to use your Let It Go Exercise from the Introduction if you should feel overwhelmed at any point.

We can't always choose
what happens to us,
but we can choose to be joyful.

DAY EIGHT
YOUR BODY

Through the last section, you will naturally have spent some time focusing on your body but in this section, we will look at it in more detail.

Many people have criticisms about their body; it is so easy to think it isn't good enough in some way. How many of us really love our own bodies, even our wrinkles and bulges? How often do we acknowledge how much work every part of our body does daily and how wonderful it is?

One of the best ways for us to feel joyful about our body is to appreciate what a miraculous system we have.

The human body
can overcome things
you would
never expect.

Body Facts:

- You have more than 100,000 miles of blood vessels in your body; if they were laid out end to end, they would circle the Earth four times.

- You get a new top layer of skin every thirty days.

- No matter how badly fingerprints get damaged, they will always grow back in the same pattern.

- People have a unique odor—apart from identical twins who have the same odor.

- Your stomach acid can dissolve metal.

- Fifty percent of your hand strength comes from your little finger.

- The human brain has a memory capacity equivalent to more than 4 terabytes on a hard drive.

- 50,000 cells in your body died and were replaced by new ones as you were reading this sentence.

- If human hair was allowed to grow unchecked, it would reach about 450 miles in length after the average lifetime.

- 100,000 chemical reactions occur in the brain every second.

- The average human eye can distinguish up to 10 million different colors.

Your body is the harp of your soul and it is yours to bring forth sweet music from it.

Kahlil Gibran

On this page make a note of the facts you found most interesting and why. What else does it make you want to find out about your body? Research a few more incredible facts about the human body and then add in those facts below.

AFFIRMATION:

My amazing body
fills me with joy.

SHORT BODY EXERCISE

Sit or lie in a comfortable position, then close your eyes and relax. Take a few deep, slow breaths.

Now consider this fact that you know now: You get a new layer of top skin every thirty days. Think about all the skin that covers your body. Go through all your limbs and body parts, thinking about your skin in each area.

How often do you appreciate its structure, shape, and strength? Think about how it protects you and how flexible it is.

Now open your eyes and really study different areas of skin: your fingertips, your elbow, your stomach, your leg, your foot. It can be whatever part you feel drawn to. You don't have to study any areas of your body that make you feel challenged or uncomfortable. Focus on the areas that fill you with wonder and surprise, and really study your skin. Notice the different textures and colors.

Where possible smell and even taste your skin. What soft sound does it make as you rub your skin gently?

Think about how the top layer of your skin sheds very slowly, imperceptibly, and yet constantly. Every month, you have a new skin surface, a fresh covering over and over for your amazing body. Give thanks for this wonderful process that takes place without you having to do anything.

When you are ready, give your body a gentle shake and stretch out your muscles before you make your notes.

What touched you most when you stopped to think deeply and thoroughly examine your own skin? What parts of your skin were most revealing to you? Which one of your senses felt most alive? Make comments about how wonder and appreciation can be linked to joy. Also make notes about what other parts of your body you could stop and appreciate in a joyful way.

LONGER BODY EXERCISE

Sit upright or lie down in a comfortable position. Give yourself time to settle and relax, focusing on your breathing for a few minutes before you start.

Now consider this fact that you know now: 50,000 cells are replaced in your body every few seconds. How does knowing that make you feel? Where in your body do you feel it?

Now focus first of all on your skin covering your body. Consider how it protects and supports all your muscles and bone. Pause a while to give thanks for its amazing structure and flexibility, as well as its strength. Stroke your skin in different areas if you wish, really look at the myriad of colors and textures on different parts of your body. Taste and/or smell your skin. Lift one hand up to an ear and gently brush it with your other hand. What is the sound like? Keeping your hands near an ear, gently stroke the inner wrist of one hand with one finger of your other hand. How does the sound differ?

When you are ready, relax back into a comfortable position. Close your eyes. Now you are going to take a journey further inward. Travel slowly through the skin's layer and consider your muscles, bones, and veins. What tasks do they perform constantly for you? Think about your organs and how each undertakes separate actions to ensure your body keeps operating smoothly. Let yourself be filled with awe for your extraordinary body. Enjoy any sensations that come to you as you do this.

Now keep going deeper as if you had a microscope and travel through your body tissue into the cells within that tissue. Realize that within the cells are even smaller elements: molecules and atoms. Think about the fact that more than 35 trillion cells exist in your body. We are so complex and so beautiful.

Try to imagine 50,000 of those cells disappearing and new ones being created. How does that make you feel? What thoughts come into your head? What images are you seeing? Observe any sounds, scents, smells, or tastes too.

Stay in that state of wonder for as long as you can and then slowly focus on being back in the room again. Open your eyes, give a slow, long stretch, and really notice how your body feels right now. Wait until you feel grounded before you start making notes.

Start your notes with what you experienced during your skin exploration. Remember all your senses and what they discovered. Make a note if one sense was more active than another. Then try to recall everything you felt and thought about your cells renewing. What images did you see? What sounds? Enjoy remembering your thoughts and feelings as you write up how your journey inward was for you.

The mindful exploration and appreciation of your body can continue effortlessly with almost anything you do. The simple act of picking up a drink can become a moment of joy when you think about how your fingers and hands are making connections with your brain to allow all these actions to happen. Washing your face and hands becomes more pleasurable when done mindfully. Literally any task you do can be appreciated more when you really appreciate your body. Enjoy your experiences.

The deeper level after this is to appreciate the parts of your body with which you feel less affection. We all have those. If you want to practice that, remember to be gentle with yourself and to use the Let It Go Exercise in the Introduction if you need to.

We celebrate the wonders of technology, yet how often do we pause to appreciate the wondrous technology that is our human body?

DAY NINE
NATURE

When you read books about mindfulness they usually mention nature. Why is this? If you consider that mindfulness means simply to "be in the moment," then appreciation of nature is a wonderful way to let go of stress and unwanted thoughts. How often do you hear someone say: "I went for a walk to clear my head?" Just a few brief minutes of nature appreciation every day can reduce stress, lower blood pressure, and put a smile on your face.

You can do it simply too. If you live in the city, you don't have to find a park (although that would be lovely). You can appreciate a houseplant or even a weed in a sidewalk. You can close your eyes and listen to the wind in the trees. If you're working in the office, you can put on a recording of birdsong or ocean waves and let yourself be immersed in the sounds of nature.

So there are easy ways to appreciate nature even if we can't access nature itself immediately.

Nature is painting for us,
day after day,
pictures of infinite beauty.

John Ruskin

Look deep into nature
and you will understand
everything better.

Albert Einstein

AFFIRMATION:

Nature
replenishes
my joy.

SHORT NATURE EXERCISE

Choose a plant or flower that you can have in front of you. Sit or stand and relax, taking several deep breaths.

Start simply by looking at your chosen gift from nature. Look closely. What colors, shapes, and textures are you seeing? How many different colors and shapes? What patterns are you noticing?

When you feel you have seen everything there is to see, then touch it gently all over. What does it feel like? How are parts of it different to the touch? Try brushing it against your cheek. How does that feel?

Smell the plant or flower on a deep inbreath. Then take an even deeper breath. What extra scent do you notice on the second breath? If you can taste it safely, do so. Is there a sound with this object?

How did this plant or flower come into being? As you keep appreciating it, think about its journey from inception to where it is with you now. How long has this species of plant/flower been in existence? Hundreds or thousands of years? How has it survived? How has it evolved? It doesn't matter that you may not know the answers. Just enjoy thinking about its tenacity and endurance over time.

Stroke or kiss it if you wish as you finish this exercise.

Make notes about what aspect of the exercise gave you the most joy and why. If your experience has made you curious, try to find out more about the plant/ flower you chose: its history, its cultivation. Write down below what you discovered and how it makes you feel. What other plants and flowers would you like to enjoy the same way?

Here are some amazing facts about nature and our planet Earth:

- Plants have existed on the surface of the Earth for around 400 million years.

- The oldest pocket of water ever found was 2.6 billion years old. It was found in a mine two miles below the Earth's surface.

- Trees in a forest can "talk" by sharing their nutrients through soil fungi via their roots.

- Moon flowers will only bloom at night when the moon is out.

- There may be as many as 10 billion solar systems in the Milky Way.

- Our planet Earth is about 4.5 billion years old.

- Ninety-four percent of the Earth's living species exist within our oceans.

- The world's largest chain of mountains (the Mid-Ocean Ridge) is under water and stretches for 65,000 km, more than 40,000 miles.

There are more things in
heaven and earth, Horatio,
than are dreamt of in
your philosophy.

William Shakespeare: Hamlet

LONGER NATURE EXERCISE

Find a natural setting where you can walk, undisturbed if possible. Time among nature can be a joyous assault on all your senses if you let it. As you have now done exercises involving all your senses, let yourself wander slowly through your chosen area and actively allow all your senses to come alive. Really take your time.

Walk barefoot through grass or water, or whatever surface is available to you. Stop and smell everything around you. Notice how different and complex the various odors are. Touch nature in all its different forms. Run your fingers over different surfaces; put things to your cheek if you like. Hug a tree if you can. What are all the sounds you can hear? Close your eyes and listen closely. What is safe for you to taste? Really look closely at what is around you. Stop and examine the grass or soil or water. What can you see? What creatures are there? What colors can you find? What shapes are being made in nature?

Look up to the sky. What does it look like? Perhaps lie down and study the sky properly. Lie down under a tree and watch light filtering through the leaves.

Find what appeals to you—and your senses—by slow and gentle exploration. When something gives you that deep feeling of joy, linger there and experience it fully.

Take your time when you withdraw from your foray into nature. Don't be surprised if it takes you a while to acclimatise again.

Make notes below of what gave you the greatest joy. What senses came alive for you the most? It is fine if you didn't enjoy some aspects or if some parts of nature didn't seem to touch you deeply. If you found that everything did, that is fine too. This is your own personal journey. Everyone experiences nature differently. Learn what really works for you.

Finding joy in nature doesn't have to be a short or infrequent exercise. Any interaction you have with nature can bring you joy. I take longer watering my plants now—both indoor and outdoor—because I stop to appreciate each plant. I run my fingers over the fragrant ones such as my lavender and thank them for their scent. I check for dead leaves and twisted stems and try to make sure each plant is as comfortable as possible. I soak in their bright colors with my eyes. I love hearing the wind rustling the plant leaves and the sound the water makes as it splashes on to the soil. Sometimes I feel I can hear the plants say "thank you" in their silent language! Watering has become a joy.

Find your own joy in nature by working out what activities rejuvenate and uplift you the most. List them here.

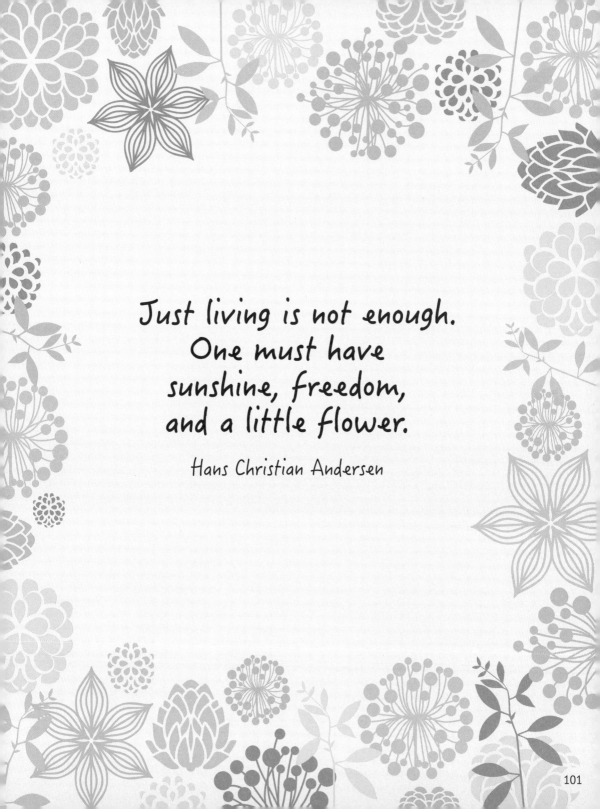

Just living is not enough.
One must have
sunshine, freedom,
and a little flower.

Hans Christian Andersen

DAY TEN
CREATURES

There are so many creatures, both wild and domesticated. Having been brought up with animals, I have always found in them a form of happy mindfulness. I would watch my cats cleaning themselves, my dog lying in the garden, or my sister's horse cantering freely and then rolling in a field. An unexpected sense of "everything is alright in the world" would wash over me and make me smile.

Creatures are important to study because all they know is mindfulness. They don't worry about the past or the future. They simply exist in the here and now, reacting to what is around them. So by observing and being around them, they can inspire us to be the same way.

What animals are you drawn to naturally? Why do you think that is?
List them below and why you like them.

Interesting Creature Facts:

- Muriqui monkeys love to hug each other, often starting their day with a group hug.

- There were sharks on Earth before there were trees.

- Dolphins can remain awake for a long time, by resting half of their brain at a time.

- Flocks of birds flying have no one "leader." Their movement is a collective energy with each bird reacting to the merest change of direction from its neighbor, almost as if they were all one consciousness.

- Some male songbirds sing more than 2,000 times a day.

- Insects don't have lungs.

- Seahorses mate for life and hold each other's tails when traveling.

- Elephant trunks, despite weighing up to 400 lbs, are dextrous enough to pick up a single grain of rice.

- A nine-year-old cat will have spent six of its years sleeping.

- Petting your pet dog as you look into its eyes can raise oxytocin levels in you both: It's a "feel good" chemical.

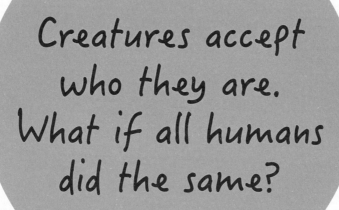

Creatures accept
who they are.
What if all humans
did the same?

Animals are such
agreeable friends —
they ask no questions,
they pass no criticisms.

George Eliot

SHORT CREATURE EXERCISE

Sit comfortably and close your eyes. Focus on your breathing and allow the word "joy" to flow in and out of you.

When you are ready, allow your thoughts to focus on a creature to which you feel drawn naturally. It doesn't matter if you have been in physical contact with it or not, just that you feel a connection with the creature in some way.

Picture the creature in front of you. What is your first sensation when you do this? What are you curious about? Allow the image to become clear in front of you. What colors, shapes, and movement are you seeing? What would happen if you touched this creature? Or smelled it? Or licked it? What sounds does it make?

Observe what is happening in your body as you experience this creature as much as you can. Where are you feeling the wonderment, the joy? What aspect of it appeals to you most? Why?

Ask yourself why you chose this creature to focus upon. Notice the answer and how it makes you feel.

When you are ready, let the image of the creature slowly dissolve in front of you. Open your eyes and make sure your body feels comfortable and grounded, before you write your notes.

What new things did you discover about your chosen creature? If you found similarities between you and it, that is fine. You may feel it had something to teach you. What gave you the greatest sense of wonder and joy? Why? What other creatures does it make you want to get to know in a more mindful way? You may want to do some research to discover more about the creature you chose. Write below what you discover and why that resonates with you.

Before moving on to the Longer Creature Exercise, let us spend a little time appreciating how creatures live only in a natural state of mindfulness. This is a profound realization when you really think about it. Humans tend to be so caught up in past or future events that it is very hard to grasp how we could live totally in the here and now—and yet it seems animals do just that.

One of the best ways to appreciate this is to observe creatures doing something simple and to see how they are totally absorbed in their task without distraction.

As this book is about joy, I'd like to suggest you watch animals playing and relaxing to appreciate fully their sense of pleasure. You can do this in any number of ways. Here are a few suggestions:

- dogs playing fetch or greeting other doggie friends
- cats playing with string or a toy
- birds sunbathing
- horses cantering freely
- moon bears playing with each other
- dolphins swimming in their natural habitat
- lion cubs play-fighting

In fact, any creature can be a joy to watch at play and relaxation, depending upon your personal attraction. Playful tendencies have been found in so many creatures, including rats, wasps, turtles, and spiders! So choose a creature that you enjoy studying.

If you can't watch any creatures in real life, look at videos. There are plenty available for you to appreciate. (I would suggest you avoid animals in confined environments such as zoos, because their behaviour is altered through captivity. Experienced rescue centres are different as they can gear the animal's welfare to their individual needs.)

People may talk to animals, but how many listen to them?

Experiencing joy in creatures is particularly wonderful because of the mindful way they are totally absorbed in their activity. For example, have you ever watched a dog playing fetch? Their focus on the ball is complete; nothing else seems to exist in their universe apart from their focus on it and their joy in playing.

Another series of videos I find particularly fascinating and uplifting is the one featuring rescued moon bears in the Animals Asia charity. The majority of the bears come from years of unimaginable torture and confinement, yet their ability to rediscover mindful play is so strong. To see such traumatized creatures regain their sense of joy is uplifting and gives hope to us as humans, especially those who have suffered great loss and hardship.

This seems to provide proof that mindfulness can help us to find joy again, no matter what we have been through.

LONGER CREATURE EXERCISE

Sit comfortably and close your eyes. Focus on your breathing and the word "joy" for a few minutes.

Reflect back through the examples you have watched of creatures playing. What gave you the most joy to watch?

Now focus your attention on the creature you have chosen. Play its antics over in your mind's eye and allow the images to become vivid and real in front of you. What are you seeing? What sounds are you hearing? What is it making you feel and where are you feeling it?

When you feel the scene is fully alive for you, step into the images themselves. Let yourself become part of the play and joy. How is that making you feel? Remember to use all your senses where possible: sight, hearing, smell, taste, and touch. Allow yourself to feel whatever you want and notice where in your body you are feeling it. Let thoughts come and go through you without trying to hold on to any of them.

If you want to take one step further, imagine yourself actually becoming the creature. Step into their body and see how that makes you feel. What are you thinking now?

Enjoy the experience for as long as you wish and then slowly remove yourself from the creature and then the scene itself. Let the scene fade slowly from your mind's eye. When you are ready, open your eyes and focus on the space in which you are sitting now. Give your feet a gentle stamp on the ground and stretch your muscles. Take a moment to reorient yourself before you start making notes.

It is fine if you experienced a lot during this exercise, and it is also fine if you found it difficult. This is your own personal journey. Be honest as you describe how you felt. Remember to cover why you chose the creature you did, what the scene and images were, how you felt as you watched the scene, then joined in, and lastly became the creature itself. What part of the exercise gave you the greatest joy? How do you think animal joy differs from human joy?

Once you really appreciate the mindfulness of creatures—how they simply don't know how to be any other way—it can be inspirational. Don't be surprised if you find yourself wanting more animal influences around you. If you repeat this section with different creatures, you will start to understand on a profound level why you are drawn naturally to certain species. Often this is because we have something to learn or appreciate from them, which in turn helps us to live our lives in a more meaningful and joyful way.

And if you have the opportunity to interact physically with other creatures, do so in a mindful way. There are few things more relaxing than watching a creature fully relax. They seem to do so with every fibre of their being and it can be joyous to watch. Watch a cat cleaning itself mindfully—how often do we as humans clean our own body in that way, even though we don't have to use our tongues because we have the luxury of different cleansing materials?!

To increase your joyfulness quota, no matter how briefly, include animal appreciation somewhere in your daily activity.

DAY ELEVEN
GRATITUDE

You will probably have realized by now that feeling gratitude has become an integral part of your joyful experience. Why is this?

Some people might say gratitude and joy are quite similar, but I believe the feeling of gratitude is the first step and joy is the outcome. It is possible to be grateful for what you have—and many indeed are—but you might stop there and not go on to experience great joy. Why is that?

I think it is worth exploring the word "gratitude" and what it means to you, so you can understand your connection with joy more deeply.

Write down below what the word "gratitude" means to you. Use as many adjectives as you wish, describe as many meanings as you want. Make this a painting if you wish! (At the end of this section, I have shared what came up for me when I did this exercise, so you may not want to read that until you have done this for yourself.)

Remember there are no right or wrong answers here, just your experience. If I suggest increasing your sense of gratitude on a daily basis, you might take that as yet another task that you need to fit in to your already crowded day. I could understand you finding that frustrating.

Once we perceive mindful activity as a chore, any joy is automatically taken out of it. So the Short Gratitude Exercise coming up is a simple way of approaching it that might make it feel easier.

SHORT GRATITUDE EXERCISE

This short exercise is something you need to do throughout the day—or at least throughout part of the day—but I promise it is very quick! It is also very simple.

From the time you wake up, say a quick and silent "thank you" for anything for which you feel grateful. It doesn't matter what it is. It can be something major that happens or it can be the smallest moment. You can say it a hundred times or just once or twice.

If you find it distracting, limit yourself to a time frame and commit to it within that time frame, even if it is just for a few minutes of the day. Some people wake up intending to do it and then forget as the day wears on. Some find their "thank you's" increase as the day develops.

However it works for you is fine. Once you have completed your chosen period of time, make notes about your experience.

The first thing to notice is: Was this easy or difficult? What made it that way? How did your journey progress through the time you chose? What were your feelings about saying "thank you"? Give yourself time to think about your responses. Notice your emotions as you did this. What percentage of the time did you feel joy with your "thank you's"? Write down some, or all, of the things for which you were grateful. How do you feel about those things now?

This exercise can be done at any time, of course. You don't have to restrict yourself to a time frame. You might just want to do it as and when you think of it. What is interesting to note is whether it feels like a natural part of your day or if it is a conscious effort.

AFFIRMATION:

I feel gratitude every day.

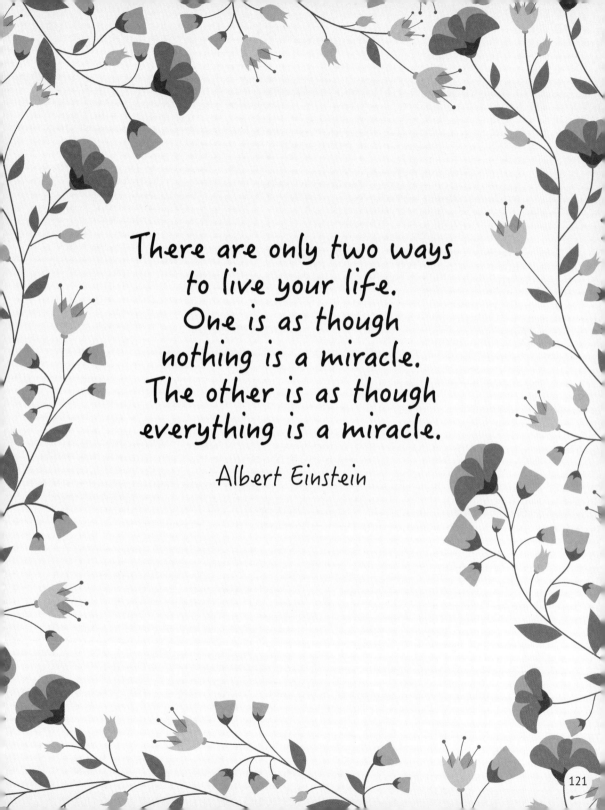

There are only two ways
to live your life.
One is as though
nothing is a miracle.
The other is as though
everything is a miracle.

Albert Einstein

LONGER GRATITUDE EXERCISE

Sit or lie comfortably and close your eyes. Focus on your breathing for a few minutes, remembering not to force your breath but to relax into it. Breathe in the word "joy" and let it filter through you.

Now say silently to yourself "being grateful fills me with joy." Observe what happens to you when you say it first. Now repeat it, more slowly. Notice any differences. If you feel sensations, where are they in your body? Wash them away and refocus.

Next say the word "gratitude" silently or out loud. What does it make you think? What does it make you feel? Take your time. Then let those thoughts and feelings go.

Now focus on the word with which you are so familiar now: "joy." Let the word run through you. What are you feeling? Focus on what is real for you right now. Then ask yourself this question: How does it differ from the energy of the word "gratitude"?

Remain relaxed and let the information come to you. It doesn't matter what you get.

When you are ready, withdraw your focus from the words and open your eyes. Write in your journal as soon as you are ready.

Make separate headings of "being grateful fills me with joy," "gratitude," and "joy." Then have a further heading: "differences." Write down everything you can remember without censoring yourself and once you have done that, read back to see what you have learned. With which did you have the strongest reaction? Why? And notice what the differences mean to you.

For some, the differences in the energy of the words are subtle; for others they are profound. Be honest with what is true for you.

The link between gratitude and joy is a strong one. If you find it difficult to feel grateful, you may find it harder to experience joy.

One of the great aspects of increasing your gratitude is how it pulls you into the here and now, which is true mindfulness. You can't fret about the future or what you don't have if you are busy being grateful for what you do have. And the more you are grateful for everything around you, the more joy will burst into your life. There is no downside to having gratitude; encourage it as much as you can.

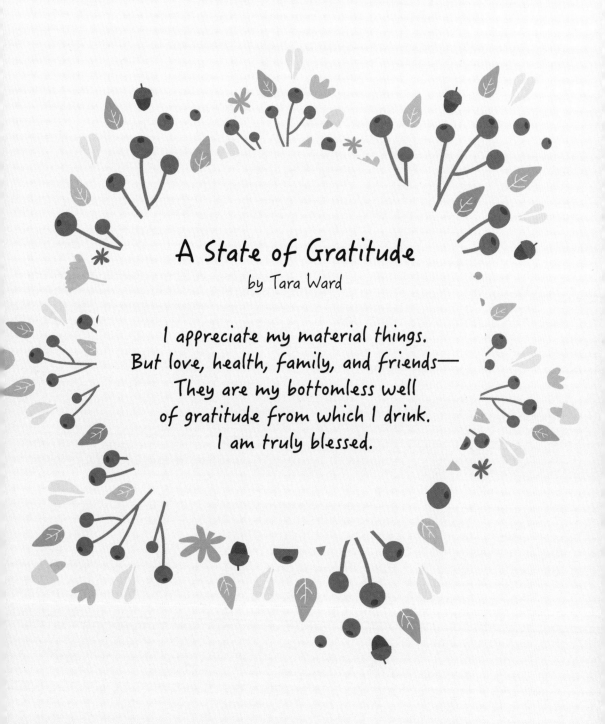

A State of Gratitude
by Tara Ward

I appreciate my material things.
But love, health, family, and friends—
They are my bottomless well
of gratitude from which I drink.
I am truly blessed.

As promised, here is my list of words when I thought about the word "gratitude." It doesn't matter if you had some or none of these words yourself. It is just fun to compare and notice!

Appreciation

Positivity

Kindness

A Way of Living

Connecting

Calm

Peace

Stillness

Acceptance

Effortless

Comforting

Smiles

Goodness

Profound
Happiness

Smoothing the
Bumps

Now add your own:

DAY TWELVE
LOVE

Love is such an emotive word and it may mean different things to different people. So this section is about you exploring your own personal relationship with love and seeing how it links to joy.

Who or what do you love, as opposed to simply like? Write below what you love.

There is no right or wrong thing to have listed. Some people might think it isn't really right to love something material, but I disagree. It depends what that object means to you. To give a personal example, when my late husband was struggling with years of chemo, one thing that always brought him great joy was driving in his second-hand, open-top convertible. When we meandered through country lanes with the car roof open, it gave him freedom from his challenges and he felt alive. I gave thanks for his car every time we got into it and I was profoundly sad when I sold it after his death. So I loved that car because of what it symbolized for my husband. Love can come in different forms.

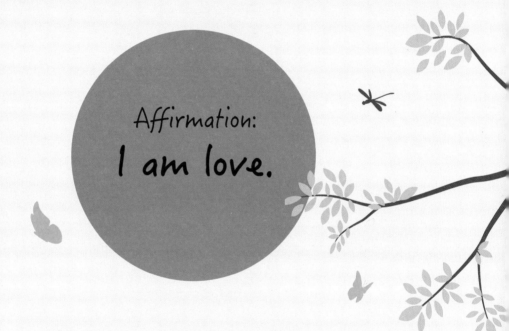

Affirmation:
I am love.

Love is inside us all and
by releasing it to others
we can ease suffering
and bring great joy.

SHORT LOVE EXERCISE

Sit comfortably and close your eyes. Focus on your breathing for a few minutes.

Now breathe in and say the word "love." As you breathe out, repeat the word. Keep doing this for several breaths. Notice what you are thinking and feeling.

As you sit there, relaxed and breathing comfortably, think about all your senses and how they can react to this word. Take your time with this. What do you see when you say "love?" What do you hear? What does it taste like? What is its smell? If you could touch love, what would the touch be like?

Notice how you are feeling as you finish going through your senses. Where in your body are you having any sensations? Think about how you would describe them. Observe what thoughts are going through your mind.

Now wash away the word "love," let it go using whatever technique you like, and then finish by saying the word "joy." Breathe it in and out several times. How does that make you feel and think?

When you are ready, slowly open your eyes and take a minute before you write in your journal.

As you write, try to recall how each of your senses reacted to the word "love." Note which responses were stronger. Recall if you had any sensations in your body and where they were. Also record how you reacted to the word "joy" at the end. Were your responses similar or quite different? Why do you think that is?

Love has many sensations. It can be passionate. It can throb gently. Sometimes it can be soft and calm. Write down a list of the things you love and how they make you feel/think.

LONGER LOVE EXERCISE

Sit or lie comfortably. Close your eyes. Take your time and let yourself relax. Stretch out your body, wriggle if you wish. Yawn or sigh. Allow your body to unwind and feel heavy against the surface on which it is resting.

Then start to notice your breathing. Let it come and go as it wishes. It will deepen naturally. After a few minutes, count silently one, two, three as you breathe in, hold for one, two, and then breathe out as you say one, two, three. Repeat at least three times.

Now when you breathe in, let the word "love" come into you. Breathe it in and notice where it goes in your body. How is it making you feel? What are you thinking? Notice what it looks, sounds, tastes, smells, and feels like. Take your time.

When you are ready to move on, say: "I am love," out loud if you can. Say it slowly and repeat it a few times. Observe what happens without trying to alter it in any way. Where in your body are you feeling sensations? Stay in this state for as long as you feel comfortable. Let go of anything you don't want to hold on to.

Lastly, focus on something or someone in your list that you wrote at the start of this section. Think of them or the object, say the word "love" and allow yourself to respond however feels right for you. Take your time.

When you are ready, withdraw from the object or person by letting the energy go. Feel, see or sense it receding into the distance. Open your eyes, give your body a pleasant stretch, and allow yourself a few moments before you write in your journal.

This exercise has a lot of elements to it and might make you feel very emotional. Remember to let go of anything you don't wish to hold on to. If you felt very little, that is fine too. Take your time as you write your notes. Try to remember the different elements and how you responded to each: the word "love," saying "I am love," and then focusing on the person or object at the end. Remember you can draw instead if words don't come to you.

This section may bring up more emotions for you than the other exercises. If this is true for you, please be gentle with yourself. The art of mindfulness is not to rush but to let things be just as they are. You are on a journey that has no end and it can be taken at whatever pace you choose. Rest here a while, retracing any elements of the Love exercises that feel right for you. Take your time. Be kind to yourself.

Spend time reflecting on the words "love" and "joy" and how they connect for you personally. How different does it feel experiencing these words on a deeper level through mindfulness?

Move on to Day Thirteen only when you are ready.

The more
we love,
the greater
our joy.

DAY THIRTEEN
EXPANSION

You have spent some time now in a wide variety of exercises, being encouraged to look at and experience joy in a mindful way. By this stage, you may be feeling more enlightened, more joyful and/or more confused! Any response is right. If you have been able to take your time and go through each section slowly and thoroughly, you may be surprised by some of the experiences you had. The more we allow ourselves to go fully into mindfulness, the more we uncover.

> We cannot solve the world's problems, but we can choose to be joyful every day.

Is this true? It can be hard to find joy in difficult times. And mindfulness is about being in the here and now, acknowledging what is happening for you at any given moment. So I don't believe it is realistic to live in a permanent state of joy if you are living mindfully.

However, there are opportunities to find more joy in everything we do if we shift our mindset. Joy can be found in the simplest things as you will have discovered already through various exercises.

So how can you expand that to reach out into more areas of your life, without it being an effort? That is what we are going to explore in this section.

Your exploration of this will be a personal one, because there is no one way to increase joy in your life. What works for one person may leave someone else uninspired.

So your first task in this section is to think back through all the exercises you have done and decide what areas were most powerful for you. You might know this immediately or you might need to flick back and reread some of your journal. Choose one area or exercise you can revisit that gave you a lot of joy. Reread that section of your journal.

Now reflect on an area with which you struggled more. You might think now that you understand why but it also doesn't matter if you aren't sure. Choose one exercise to revisit. Reread your journal notes on it.

Whatever you choose
to focus upon
will expand.

SHORT EXPANSION EXERCISE

Sit comfortably and close your eyes. Take a little longer than usual to relax and focus on your breathing.

When you are ready focus on the exercise with which you experienced the greatest joy. Let yourself enjoy the moment again. Bask in its memory and even replay it fully if you want. As you do this, ask yourself why it gives you such joy. Breathe deeply and comfortably and see what answers come to you. Take your time. You may be surprised by the answers. Fully experience your joy. Let it expand. When you are ready, let go of this memory using whatever technique you like.

Focus again on your breathing for a few moments.

Now focus on the exercise with which you found the least joy. Let it replay again for you and as it does, ask yourself what you could do to expand your joy in this exercise. You may notice your answers from your previous exercise help you or you may find different information coming to you. Remember to keep breathing deeply and relaxing. This can be effortless; discovering more about yourself is a joy in itself. You may find your joy expanding with this exercise as you understand what is happening. Enjoy it. Then, when you are ready, slowly let go of the memory.

Wait a few minutes before you open your eyes and reorient yourself.

This exercise can serve as a gentle enquiry into blocks you may be encountering on your journey into mindful joy. Each of us has them in different areas. What have you discovered about yourself? Make notes. Be honest. What insights have you got now about how to expand your joy in other ways? If you feel stuck, write about that and why you think you're stuck. Remember, wherever you are right now is fine.

Before we go on to the Longer Expansion Exercise, let us focus on something I have touched on several times: That we can choose consciously to be more joyful if we wish, irrespective of our circumstances. That can be a tough aspect to grasp if we are not used to thinking that way, and many of us aren't. If someone is struggling with a lot of challenges, that can make it hard to accept also.

Affirmations can help a lot and if you have been using them, you may have discovered this already. If you haven't, try saying them more frequently. Repeat an affirmation at least ten times in a row and at least ten times a day. A simple affirmation that can be highly effective is simply:

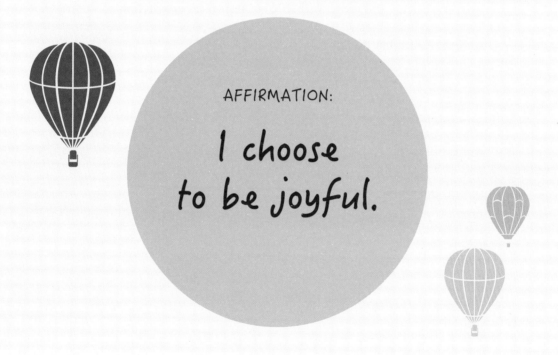

AFFIRMATION:

I choose
to be joyful.

Another way we can expand our state of mindful joy is to imagine our joyful energy increasing—literally. If this thought appeals to you, try the next exercise.

LONGER EXPANSION EXERCISE

Sit or lie comfortably and close your eyes. Take as long as you can to relax and deepen your breathing. Remember to make it effortless: Observe your breath first of all without trying to change it in any way, then let it deepen of its own accord without trying. If it helps you to count up to three as you breathe in, hold for two, and then breathe out for three, do this. Take your time.

When you feel fully relaxed, breathe in the word "joy" and breathe it out. Do this several times.

Now focus on an exercise you chose that made you feel particularly joyful. Let it replay again for you. Let yourself experience that joy again, however you want to. It can be an image, sound, smell, taste, touch, feeling—any or all of these.

Become aware of the edges of your physical body. Are you breathing the sensation into all of your body? Take your time and allow your whole physical body to fill with your joy. Notice how this is making you feel. Go through all of your body, right to the extremities of your toes and fingers, and breathe your joy into every area, so you experience joy coursing right through every fiber of your body.

If you have a sound for your joy, imagine that sound increasing in richness and intensity, feel the sound filling your body. If it's a taste, let the taste grow and become stronger. If it's a smell, imagine that beautiful smell filling not just your nostrils but all of you. If you experience joy as a visual image inside of you, imagine that image expanding and filling all of you.

Now, if you wish and if it feels comfortable, you can imagine it expanding even more, spreading outside your body, and filling the area around you, with whatever image, sound, smell, taste, or feeling that feels right for you. Enjoy that expansion for as long as you can.

When you are ready, slowly draw your energy back in. Feel your expansion shrinking again, back to a size that is right for you. This is different for everyone so work out what feels comfortable for you.

You may choose to hold on to some of that joy or you may choose to let it go, when you slowly open your eyes and readjust to the space around you. Make notes in your journal.

You may have found this expansion a natural and pleasant experience; others may have felt less comfortable. Whatever you felt is fine. Write down how it was for you. Notice the areas that felt good and increased your joy and those that didn't work so well for you. Which of your senses made joy the most powerful and the most enjoyable?

Lastly, before we leave this section, there is time for you to reflect on what other ways you might want to expand your joy. You have covered a lot of topics in these 13 sections—but what else would you like to explore?

You may find some thoughts have been building already in your mind but you haven't written them down. What tasks or experiences when done mindfully would give you joy? There are many aspects of body (exercise) and voice (singing) we haven't touched upon. What interaction with nature or animals could you enjoy more fully? How might you use all your senses in a way that increases your joy? In what way could more expressions of love enhance your life? Reflect upon the fact that a child's energy is often full of mindful joy; how can you rediscover that in you?

Write any ideas you have below and commit to trying them in the near future.

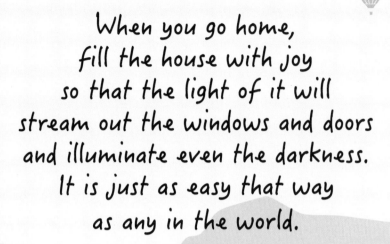

When you go home,
fill the house with joy
so that the light of it will
stream out the windows and doors
and illuminate even the darkness.
It is just as easy that way
as any in the world.

Robert Green Ingersoll

DAY FOURTEEN
JOY

Well done on reaching the last day in your Joy of Mindfulness journal!
Of course this doesn't have to be the end and I hope it isn't. I hope you feel
you are now on a pleasant journey of increasing mindful joy in your life in an
ever-expanding radius.

One of the loveliest repercussions of tapping into your mindful joy is the
energy you create around you. I love this quote below that I think is very
much about mindful joy.

> There are souls in this world
> who have the gift of finding
> joy everywhere, and leaving
> it behind them when they go.
>
> Frederick William Faber

It is not your duty to try to make others happy and this book is about YOUR joy but how nice that it may easily rub off and inspire or uplift others! Joy is contagious so feel free to spread it around if you wish.

Scatter joy!

Remember also that joy is not exclusively for happy times. As I have shared personally, even in great sadness there are opportunities for moments of profound joy. Stop, breathe, and find those moments, especially when life is chaotic.

True inner joy is self-created.
It does not depend on outer circumstances.
A river is flowing in and through you
carrying the message of joy.
This divine joy is the sole purpose of life.

Sri Chinmoy

This last section has only one exercise for everyone to enjoy so you don't have to make a choice about what you do. It is simple and quite short.

Just before you do that, I'd like to invite you to return to the very first entry you made in this journal, back on page 8 in the Introduction. How did you view the meaning of joy when you started this book? How do you feel about it now? Your journey may have been an intense one or it may have been gentle. Whatever you have experienced is right for you. Note the differences on the next page between how you felt at the start of your journaling and now.

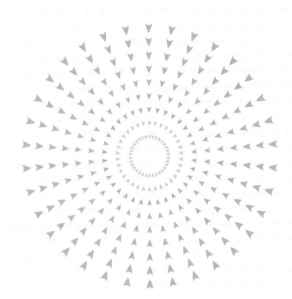

AT THE START:

NOW:

153

Infant Joy
by William Blake

'I have no name;
I am but two days old.'
What shall I call thee?
'I happy am,
Joy is my name.'
Sweet joy befall thee!

Pretty joy!
Sweet joy, but two days old.
Sweet Joy I call thee:
Thou dost smile,
I sing the while;
Sweet joy befall thee!

FINAL JOY EXERCISE

You can stand, sit or lie for this exercise. If you choose to stand, please keep your eyes open, otherwise close them if you wish.

Let yourself settle into a comfortable position. Take your time. It is often helpful to stretch or wriggle, roll your shoulders and neck, shake out your arms, yawn, or sigh. Do any or all of these things. Enjoy it.

Spend some quality time focussing on your breathing. From all your exercises so far, you will know when you are doing this fully. Really sink into the pleasure of mindful breathing now. You may yawn even more when you do this and that is a good thing. It will further relax you. This time try counting to four as you breathe in, hold for two, and then breathe out to four. If that feels too slow, revert to a three, two, three count.

When you feel relaxed and your breathing has deepened, say: "I am joy," slowly, three times. Allow the feeling to build inside and around you, however that happens for you. Let it happen gradually.

Now, open your arms out wide and repeat "I am joy," three times. Feel the joy seeping down through your arms and trickling out the tips of your fingers. Enjoy it. Stretch your arms up to the sky and again say three times: "I am joy."

Notice how your body is feeling now. Where are the sensations and what are they like?

Slowly, bring your arms back to your sides and give them a little shake. If your eyes have been closed, gently open them.

Make notes here about how you feel right now. Try to remember all your emotions and sensations. Go through all your senses to make sure you are recalling everything you can.

Very well done for this last exercise. It is one thing to experiment with different exercises to tap into joy; it is quite another level to take yourself into the state of "being" joy. If you found yourself doing just that, you were truly embracing mindful joy.

We all experience this in different ways so you needn't compare your responses to someone else's. Some may find it indescribably vivid or explosive, others will find it gentle and calming.

Often it is hard to find the right words for such a transcending experience which is why it might be helpful to use drawings if that enables you to express yourself better.

I would like to encourage you to keep returning to your exercises and trying them again. Or simply make a commitment that each day you will find several opportunities to experience mindful joy—whatever your circumstances and however small the moments. The more you make it a habit, the easier and more pleasurable it becomes.

We have reached the end of our exercises now and I feel sad to complete this book because there is so much else we could discuss.

But now you are in a powerful place to continue your personal journey of mindful joy—however it is right for you.

I wish you many moments of deep joy in your life ahead.

I choose joy
because
I am joy.